leg · foot

head · tail

Page 28

is is · a a a

wearing	hiding
purple	fuzzy
monster	scared

the the the

child
wants
from
scary

his	spiky
has	noisy
to	alien
her	cactus

Page 35

Baby Care for Beginners

Monster Book of Monsters

ALIENS vs DINOS

FOOTBALL: A HISTORY

Revenge of the Rocktopus

Page 37

Baby Bear

Mummy Bear

Daddy Bear

Page 41

Reward stickers

Alphabetical laundry

When you've finished, give yourself a reward sticker!

Pirate Pogo likes to hang his clothes in order from **a** to **z**. Find the letters in the pile and write them in the correct order on the washing line, crossing them off as you go. Some have been done for you.

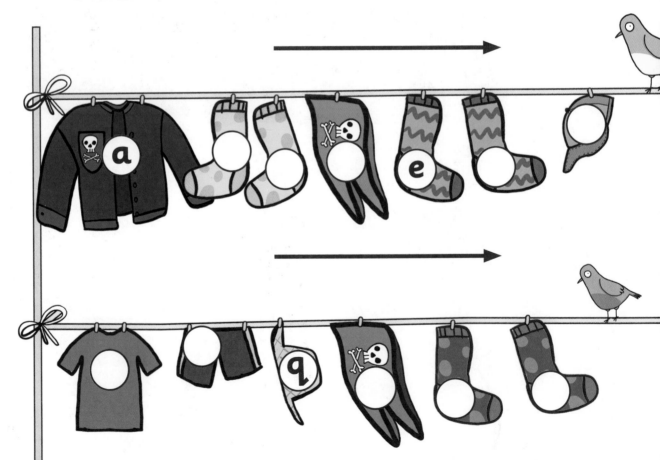

2

n d c g j

h

v i m b z

s

f o l w r q x

k a t u e p

y

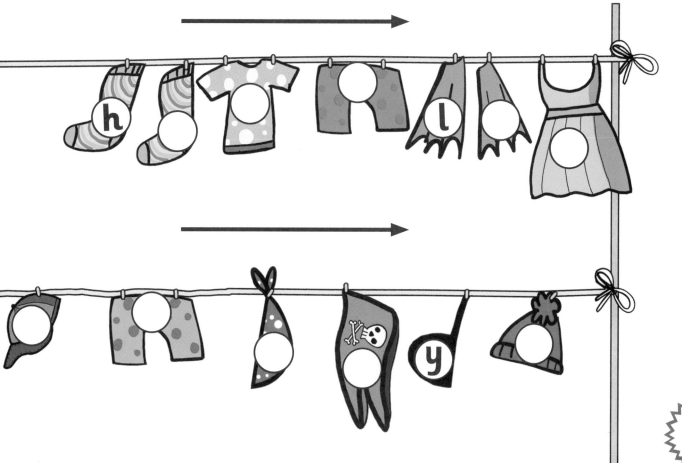

h

l

y

Answers on page 46

STICK A REWARD STICKER HERE

Match and Stick

When you've finished, give yourself a reward sticker!

Read the words out loud, sounding them out as you go. Then find the matching stickers.

can

bins

shell

cap

cup

bed

zip

map

bag

STICK A REWARD STICKER HERE

Letter pairs

The letter pairs below are digraphs; they blend together to make one sound. Complete the words by filling in the missing digraphs. Use the pictures as clues to help you. Each digraph may be used more than once.

| zz | ck | sh | ch | th | ss |

1

du__

What do you call a clever duck? A wise quacker!

2

bu__

3

dre__

4

bru__

5

fi__

6

clo__

7

slo__

8

__i__

STICK A REWARD STICKER HERE

5

Find the vowels

When you've finished, give yourself a reward sticker!

Vowels are the letters **a**, **e**, **i**, **o** and **u**. They are sounds you can sing with your mouth open. Find the vowels hiding among the letters below and colour them in. There are 15 in total.

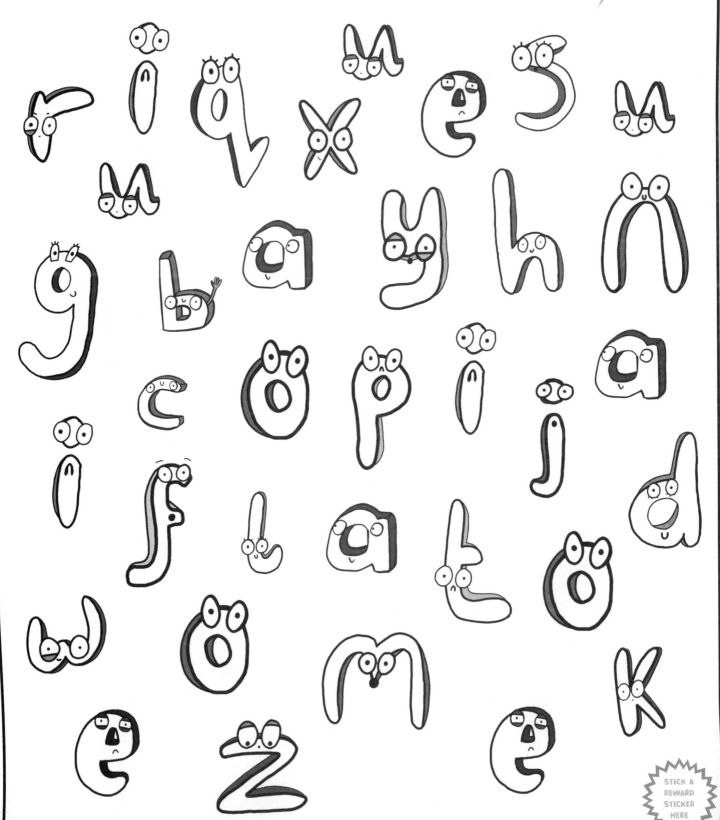

Answers on page 46

Missing vowels

Fill in the missing vowels to complete the words below. Remember, vowels are the letters **a**, **e**, **i**, **o** and **u**.

1.

p_g

2.

c_t

3.

d_g

4.

s_d

5.

h_n

6.

p_n

7.

s_n

8.

cl_ck

9.

b_s

Find the consonants

When you've finished, give yourself a reward sticker!

Consonants are letters that are not vowels: **b**, **c**, **d**, **f**, **g**, **h**, **j**, **k**, **l**, **m**, **n**, **p**, **q**, **r**, **s**, **t**, **v**, **w**, **x**, **y** and **z**. Some of them are hiding among the letters below. Find them and colour them in. There are 15 in total.

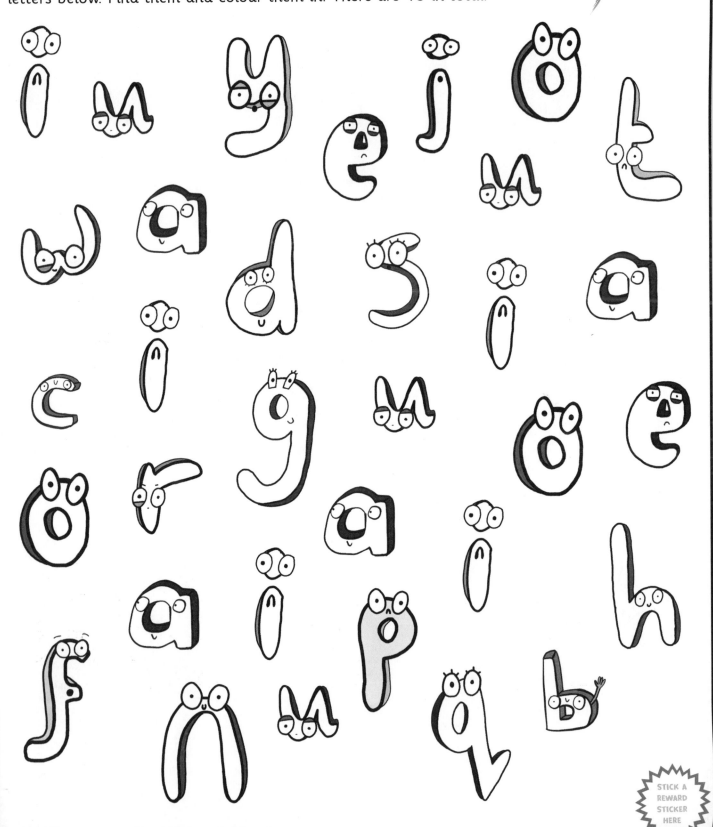

STICK A REWARD STICKER HERE

8

Write the consonants

Say the words below out loud. Then write the missing consonants.

1

_ox

2

_astle

3

_atch

4

fla_

5

cra_

6

shi_

7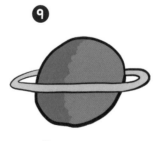

ow_

8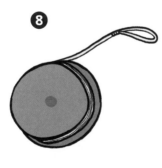

_o-yo

9

pla_et

STICK A
REWARD
STICKER
HERE

9

Missing consonants

Write the correct consonants to complete each word.

Remember, consonants are letters that are not vowels.

① ha__

② te__

③ __y

④ __eep

⑤ co__

⑥ __ail

⑦ __ee

⑧ __ain

⑨ __oon

⑩ __ider

⑪ __ush

⑫ __ick

⑬ __ag

⑭ fa__

⑮ __ile

⑯ __unk

⑰ __og

⑱ la__

11

Tricky letters

When you've finished, give yourself a reward sticker!

Some words with tricky letters are hidden in the picture below. When you spot them, fill in the missing letters from the box to complete the labels.

1

tedd_

2

fo_

3

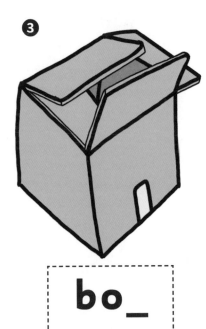

bo_

4

__een

5

s_ _irrel

12

6

_ebra

7

rainbo_

8

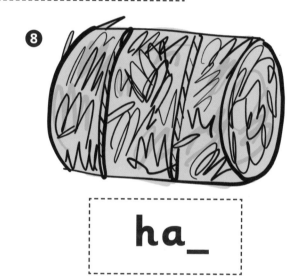

ha_

10

_ _ill

9

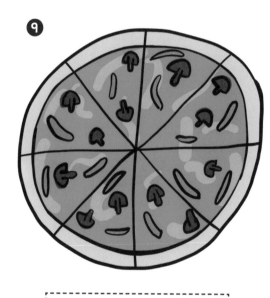

pi_ _a

z	x	w	y	qu

STICK A
REWARD
STICKER
HERE

13

Labels

When you've finished, give yourself a reward sticker!

In non-fiction writing, labels can give you more information about a picture. Choose the correct words on your sticker sheet to fill in the labels for the different parts of this giraffe.

What do you get if you cross a giraffe with a hedgehog? A twelve-foot toothbrush!

STICK A REWARD STICKER HERE

Writing labels

This time, fill in the labels by writing in the boxes. Choose from the words listed below and copy them into the correct label boxes.

| clock x-ray ears vet cat tail |

STICK A REWARD STICKER HERE

Sentences

When you've finished, give yourself a reward sticker!

Look at the pictures. Under each one is a sentence with a word missing. Choose the correct word from the list below and write it in the gap.

snake **clock**

football **apple**

❶ The unicorn is eating an

....

❷ The monkeys are playing

....

❸ The ....

is riding a skateboard.

❹ The ....

is running late.

STICK A REWARD STICKER HERE

16

More Sentences

Now copy the correct sentences beside the pictures below.

The snake does tricks on her skateboard.

This clock is always running late.

Monkeys are good football players.

The unicorn likes crunchy apples.

STICK A
REWARD
STICKER
HERE

The clown's house

When you've finished, give yourself a reward sticker!

The letter blends **ow** and **ou** can sound the same. Can you sort these **ou** and **ow** words? Fill in the missing letters, then draw a line from each of the objects to sort it into the correct box.

_ _ l

cl _ _ d

h _ _ se

m _ _ se

cr _ _ d

cr _ _ n

c _ _

What do cows like to read?

The MOO-spaper!

cl _ _ n

ou

ow

STICK A REWARD STICKER HERE

The crow's coat

Another set of letter blends that can sound the same are **oa** and **ow**. Fill in the gaps in the words, then sort the objects into the table by writing their names in the correct column.

r_ _d

sn_ _man

c_ _t

Croak

t_ _d

cr_ _

oa	ow
....	....
....	....
....	....
....	....

19

The bee's knees

When you've finished, give yourself a reward sticker!

Do you remember what sounds the digraphs **ee**, **oo** and **or** make? Use the picture clues to find 10 words with these sounds in the grid below.

❶

❷

❸

❹

❺

❿

t	o	s	t	o	r	m	t
b	o	h	r	m	k	o	n
a	e	r	e	b	o	o	k
l	t	e	t	a	b	n	i
l	c	r	t	o	r	d	l
o	n	e	e	l	i	c	b
o	k	s	f	e	e	s	e
n	t	o	r	c	h	n	e
d	i	d	o	o	r	i	s

❻

❾

❽

❼

STICK A REWARD STICKER HERE

Crossword

The letter blends **er**, **ir** or **ur** can all make the same sound. Use the pictures clues to fill in the crossword.

Clues

Across

3.

4.

6.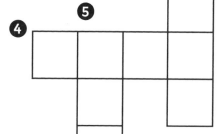

8.

Down

1.

2.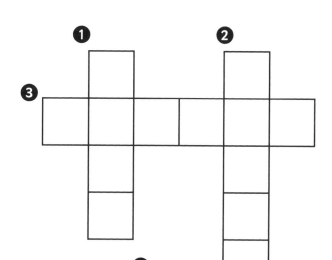

5.

7.

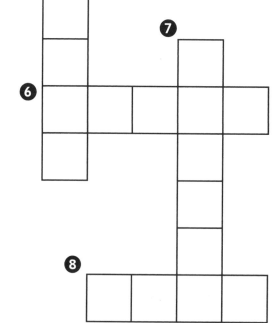

STICK A REWARD STICKER HERE

Fright night

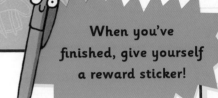
This spooky story has lots of **igh** words in it. Can you fill in the missing words, using the picture clues to help you? Choose from the words in the box.

It was a dark and stormy .... There was a big storm

with thunder and .... Rufus crept through the old,

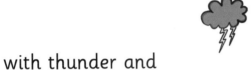

creaky house. Suddenly, he had a big .... There was a

.... at the top of the stairs. "What an awful .... !"

Rufus cried. The .... turned on the ....

"You're pretty .... , too," said the ....

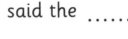

Word bank	
fright	night
lightning	knight
frightening	light
sight	

22

Answers on page 47

Say it again

This story is missing all its **ay** sounds. Write the missing letters in the gap, choosing the correct spelling from the letter blends **ay** and **ai**.

ay   ai

One r........ny Tuesd........, Burglar Bruce was on his w........

to the bank. He spotted a house with its door open.

"M........be there is something I can steal," he said. He crept inside

and saw a pile of m........l.

"Hurr........! Crime alw........s p........s," Bruce said.

He picked up the m........l. As he did, he hit a vase.

The vase sw........ed, then fell on the dog's t........l! The dog yelped

and a baby began to w........l. "Uh oh!" said Bruce. He ran away and

bumped into a policeman who had heard the w........ling.

"You ag........n!" the policeman said in dism......... "You're going to j........l."

Which Spelling?

Help the witch choose the right words to complete her magic spell by circling the correct spellings.

1 First take the croak of one warty ...

tode	toad	towd

2 Then add four rats' ...

tayls	tials	tails

3 Wait for a storm with thunder and ...

lytning	lightning	litening

4 Let the mix sit outside in the ... overnight.

rain	rayne	rayn

5 Finally, add one pink ...

mowse	mouse	mows

What's a witch's favourite subject? Spelling!

STICK A REWARD STICKER HERE

Imaginary magic

Now imagine you're a witch or wizard.

My magic name is ....

What kind of magic pet would you have?
....

My magic pet would be called ....

What would your pet help you do?

....

....

....

What would be the name of your spell?

....

What magical ingredients would you need?

....

....

....

....

What would the spell do?

....

....

....

Capital letters

When you've finished, give yourself a reward sticker!

Words that are the names of people, places or days of the week are given capital letters. These words are called proper nouns. Look at the words below and circle the ones that should have capital letters.

lola

jamaica

dolphin

ship

mars

france

scotland

marcus

whales

wales

friday

rocket

fish

What's a fish's least favourite day of the week?

Fry-day!

STICK A REWARD STICKER HERE

Answers on page 48

Now look at the sentences below and circle the words that should have capital letters.
Remember, the first word of any sentence should also start with a capital letter.

1 rome is the capital city of italy.

2 matteo is going to mars on monday.

3 whales are rare in wales.

4 polly the panda has a brother called peter.

Now write your own sentence using capital letters.
Try to include the name of a person and place.

....

....

....

....

....

STICK A
REWARD
STICKER
HERE

Full stops

When you've finished, give yourself a reward sticker!

We finish sentences with a full stop. Arrange the muddled words below into sentences, then add a full stop at the end of each one.

❶ live Penguins Antarctica in

....

❷ stair bear The ran up the

....

❸ castles You Scotland lots see of in can

....

❹ I sisters called Polly and Newt two have

....

Now use the stickers to make up your own sentences. Make sure you add a full stop at the end of each sentence. Circle any words in your sentences that need a capital letter.

....

....

....

....

....

....

STICK A REWARD STICKER HERE

Answers on page 48

Commas

We use commas for lots of different reasons. One reason is when we list things. Commas go in between the things in the list, for example: **The vet saw lots of cats, dogs, guinea pigs and lions.** Don't forget to add the word **and** before the last item in the list.

Finish each of these sentences with a list. Remember to use commas and include the word **and**.

Fido's birthday presents were ....

....

Animals invited to Fido's party were ....

....

The party snacks were ....

....

Questions and exclamations

When you've finished, give yourself a reward sticker!

We use question marks to show that we are asking something.
A question mark goes at the end of a question instead of a full stop.

How tall is the yeti?

We can also end a sentence with an exclamation
mark if we want it to have more BANG!

The yeti is enormous!

Write in question marks and exclamation marks to finish the sentences below.

Roaw!

❶ What do yetis like to eat

❷ Let's not find out

❸ What do we do

❹ Run

❺ It's over there

❻ Has it gone

❼ Eek

STICK A REWARD STICKER HERE

Answers on page 48

Apostrophes

Sometimes we push two words together to make a shortened version. We use apostrophes to show where we have missed out letters. Add apostrophes to the correct places in the shortened versions of the words below. The first two have been done for you.

① She will ⟶ She'll

② It is ⟶ It's

③ I am ⟶ Im

④ We will ⟶ Well

⑤ He is ⟶ Hes

⑥ They will ⟶ Theyll

We also use an apostrophe followed by the letter **s** to show if something belongs to someone. Add an apostrophe and the letter **s** to the words below. One has been done for you.

The giraffe's scarf

⑦ The bee__ knees

⑧ The rabbit__ hutch

⑨ The spider__ web

A Strange Safari

When you've finished, give yourself a reward sticker!

Read the passage below. Then write in the missing commas and full stops. Circle any words that should have capital letters. Underline words that have apostrophes. Can you spot any questions that should be followed by a question mark?

when Pascal was on safari,

he saw elephants lions giraffes

and a camelon. What is a camelon

These rare animals are easy to spot

because they're part camel and part

watermelon if you think that's odd,

you should see the fruit bats

STICK A REWARD STICKER HERE

Weekly words

Unscramble the letters to make the days of the week. Use the sentences as clues to help you.

Clues

On Wednesday I go swimming.   On Saturday I wash the car.

On Monday I go to school.   On Tuesday I play football.   On Sunday I have a rest.

On Thursday I go in the car.   On Friday I go shopping.

dyanoM

Monday

sueTday

Wdneesyda

uhrsTayd

yFrida

yadSurta

nSuyda

STICK A
REWARD
STICKER
HERE

33

Alphabet library

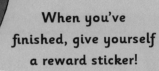

When you've finished, give yourself a reward sticker!

Organise these books into alphabetical order.

1 ....

2 ....

3 ....

4 ....

5 ....

STICK A REWARD STICKER HERE

Fiction and n0n-fiction

Use stickers to match the sentences to the book you think they come from. Then write an **F** in the box if they are fiction, or an **N** in the box if they are non fiction.

1

Zaggy Spacedust looked the evil, eight-legged rock star in the eye. "You won't win next time, Rocktopus," he vowed.

....

2

The game of football is many hundreds of years old. The first footballs were made out of pigs' bladders.

....

3

The aliens zapped their supersonic zap rays, but it was no good! The zap rays bounced off the T. rexes' scaly skin.

....

4

Around the world, four babies are born every second. Babies are much like other humans, except they are usually smaller and much, much louder.

....

STICK A
REWARD
STICKER
HERE

Comprehension

Read the story below, then answer the questions on the opposite page.

Three bears lived in a house in the forest.

One sunny morning, Daddy Bear made some porridge. They sat down to eat, but the porridge was too hot. So the three bears went out for a walk.

This porridge is too hot. Let's go for a walk.

Goldilocks was walking in the forest to visit her grandmother, when she spotted the porridge. She went inside the bears' house. First she tried Daddy Bear's porridge, but it was too hot. Then she tried Mummy Bear's porridge, but it was too cold. Finally, she tried Baby Bear's porridge. It was just right.

This porridge is just right.

After she'd eaten the porridge all up, she decided to take a nap. First she tried Daddy Bear's bed, but it was too hard. Then she tried Mummy Bear's bed, but it was too soft. Finally, she tried Baby Bear's bed. It was just right.

ZZZ.

1 Where did the bears live?

....

2 Who made the Bear family's breakfast?

....

3 Why was Goldilocks in the forest?

....

4 What did Goldilocks decide to do after she had eaten the porridge?

....

Use stickers to match
the bear to the description
of their porridge.

Just right   Too hot   Too cold

Now write an ending for the story. You can follow the fairy tale or make up
your own ending.

....

....

....

STICK A
REWARD
STICKER
HERE

37

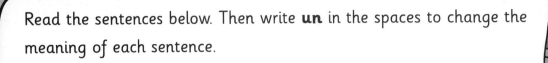
Unbelievable 'un'

Read the sentences below. Then write **un** in the spaces to change the meaning of each sentence.

When you've finished, give yourself a reward sticker!

Yesterday I was the _____ happiest girl in town.

It was the _____ tidiest room in the house.

He was always _____ friendly to the other children.

The dog never went outside and was _____ fit.

My gran tells me to eat _____ healthy food.

My dad told me off for being _____ kind.

STICK A REWARD STICKER HERE

Answers on page 48

Adding 'ed' and 'ing'

Read the story below. Add **ed** or **ing** to complete the words. When adding **ed**, watch out for words that already end in **e**!

Jack finish ____ his beans and wipe ____ the

plate with toast.

Then he look ____ at the clock. He was late!

Putt ____ on his gloves, he went out.

Soon he was runn ____ onto the football pitch.

After a few minutes, Jack score ____!

Everyone started cheer ____.

More comprehension

Read the poster for the fair below. Then answer the questions on the following page.

THE FUNTIME FAIR

IS COMING TO TOWN.

There will be
a super, swirly slide,
space-hopper races,
twirling tea-cups,
Craig the curious clown,
Brenda the balloon-modeller
and a strangely surprising surprise.

Date: Saturday 5th July
Time: 3pm
Place: Greenway Park
Price: Adults £4 Children £2

Use the information from the poster to answer the questions below by putting a thumbs up sticker in the correct box.

1 What is the name of the fair?

Funtime fair ☐   Festive fair ☐   Fun fair ☐

2 What is Brenda's job?

Clown ☐   Balloon modeller ☐   Acrobat ☐

3 What time does the fair start?

1pm ☐   2pm ☐   3pm ☐

4 How much are the children's tickets?

£2 ☐   £1.75 ☐   £4 ☐

What do you think the strangely surprising surprise might be? Use your imagination.

....

....

....

STICK A REWARD STICKER HERE

Big, Bigger

When you've finished, give yourself a reward sticker!

Compare the pictures and write the words to describe what's different about them.

Tall

Tall____

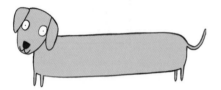

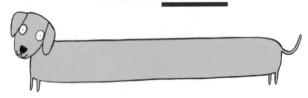

Long

Long____

Wise

Wise____

Happy

Happi____

STICK A REWARD STICKER HERE

Answers on page 48

Biggest!

Choose which word goes with each picture and write it underneath.

Longest	Smallest	Fastest
Slowest		Hungriest

....

....

....

..........Biggest!.................

....

43

What happens next?

Read the start of the story below. What do you think happens next? Continue the story yourself, using lots of description.

It was a normal Thursday afternoon. Brunhilda was walking home from her karate lesson. All of a sudden, she realised she was lost. She must have gone the wrong way in the woods. "I should go back," Brunhilda said to herself. But then she saw strange flashing lights between the trees. She went closer, and saw a group of aliens standing in front of a spaceship. They looked like they were arguing.

STICK A
REWARD
STICKER
HERE

Answers

Page 2–3: Alphabetical laundry

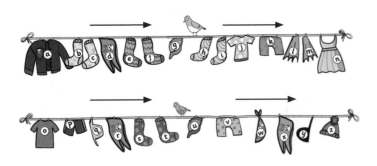

Page 5: Letter pairs
1. du**ck**, 2. bu**zz**, 3. dre**ss**, 4. bru**sh**, 5. fi**sh**, 6. clo**ck**, 7. slo**th**, 8. chi**ck**

Page 6: Find the vowels

Page 7: Missing vowels
1. p**i**g, 2. c**a**t, 3. d**o**g, 4. s**a**d, 5. h**e**n, 6. p**e**n, 7. s**u**n, 8. cl**o**ck, 9. b**u**s

Page 8: Find the consonants

Page 9: Write the consonants
1. **b**ox, 2. **c**astle, 3. **w**atch, 4. **fl**ag, 5. **cr**ab, 6. **sh**ip, 7. o**wl**, 8. **y**o-yo, 9. **pl**anet

Page 10–11: Missing consonants
1. ha**nd**, 2. te**nt**, 3. **fl**y, 4. s**l**eep, 5. co**ld**, 6. **sn**ail, 7. **tr**ee, 8. **tr**ain, 9. **sp**oon, 10. **sp**ider, 11. **br**ush, 12. **st**ick, 13. **fl**ag, 14. fa**st**, 15. s**m**ile, 16. s**k**unk, 17. **fr**og, 18. la**mp**

Page 12–13: Tricky letters
1. teddy, 2. fox, 3. box, 4. queen, 5. squirrel, 6. zebra, 7. rainbow, 8. hay, 9. pizza, 10. quill

Page 14: Labels

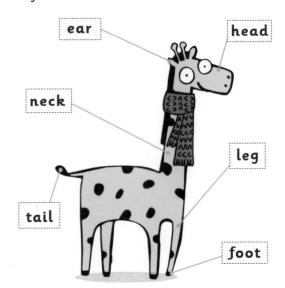

ear   head   neck   leg   tail   foot

Page 15: Writing labels

clock
ears
x-ray
tail
vet
cat

Page 16: Sentences

1. The unicorn is eating an **apple**.
2. The monkeys are playing **football**.
3. The **snake** is riding a skateboard.
4. The **clock** is running late.

Page 17: More sentences

1. The clock is always running late.
2. The snake does tricks on her skateboard.
3. The unicorn likes crunchy apples.
4. Monkeys are good football players.

Page 18: The clown's house

ou: house, mouse, cloud
ow: owl, cow, clown, crowd, crown

Page 19: The crow's coat

oa: road, coat, toad
ow: crow, snowman

Page 20: The bee's knees

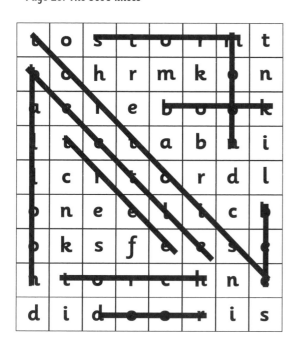

Page 21: Crossword

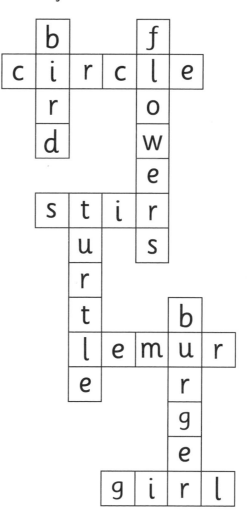

Page 22: Fright night

It was a dark and stormy **night**. There was a big storm with thunder and **lightning**. Rufus crept through the old, creaky house. Suddenly, he had a big **fright**. There was a **knight** at the top of the stairs. "What an awful **sight**!" Rufus cried. The **knight** turned on the **light**. "You're pretty **frightening**, too," said the **knight**.

Page 23: Say it again

One r**ai**ny Tuesd**ay**, Burglar Bruce was on his w**ay** to the bank. He spotted a house with its door open. "M**ay**be there is something I can steal," he said. He crept inside and saw a pile of m**ai**l. "Hurr**ay**! Crime alw**ay**s p**ay**s," Bruce said. He picked up the m**ai**l. As he did, he hit a vase. The vase sw**ay**ed, then fell on the dog's t**ai**l! The dog yelped and a baby began to w**ai**l. "Uh oh!" said Bruce. He ran aw**ay** and bumped into a policeman who had heard the w**ai**ling. "You ag**ai**n!" the policeman said in dism**ay**. "You're going to j**ai**l."

Page 24: Which spelling?

1. toad 2. tails 3. lightning 4. rain 5. mouse

Answer page

Page 26: Capital letters
Lola, **J**amaica, **M**ars, **F**rance, **S**cotland, **M**arcus, **W**ales, **F**riday

Page 27: Capital letters
1. **R**ome is the capital city of **I**taly.
2. **M**atteo is going to **M**ars on **M**onday.
3. **W**hales are rare in **W**ales.
4. **P**olly the panda has a brother called **P**eter.

Page 28: Full Stops
1. Penguins live in Antarctica**.**
2. The bear ran up the stair**.**
3. You can see lots of castles in Scotland**.**
4. I have two sisters called Polly and Newt**.**

Page 30: Questions and exclamations
1. What do yetis like to eat**?**
2. Let's not find out**!**
3. What do we do**?**
4. Run**!**
5. It's over there**!**
6. Has it gone**?**
7. Eek**!**

Page 31: Apostrophes
1. She**'**ll, 2. It**'**s, 3. I**'**m, 4. We**'**ll, 5. He**'**s, 6. They**'**ll

7. The bee**'s** knees
8. The rabbit**'s** hutch
9. The spider**'s** web

Page 32: A strange safari
When Pascal was on safari, he saw elephants**,** lions**,** giraffes and a camelon. What is a camelon**?** These rare animals are easy to spot because they're part camel and part watermelon**.** **I**f you think that's odd, you should see the fruit bats**!**

Page 33: Weekly words
dyanoM – Monday, sueTday – Tuesday, Wdneesyda – Wednesday, uhrsTayd – Thursday, yFrida – Friday, yadSurta – Saturday, nSuyda – Sunday

Page 34: Alphabet library
1. Aliens vs Dinos, 2. Baby Care for Beginners, 3. Football: A History, 4. Monster Book of Monsters, 5. Revenge of the Rocktopus.

Page 35: Fiction and non-fiction

 **F**

  **F**

 N

 N

Page 36–37: Comprehension
1. The bears lived in a house in the forest.
2. Daddy bear made the Bear family's breakfast.
3. Goldilocks was in the forest to visit her grandmother.
4. Goldilocks decided to take a nap after she had eaten the porridge.

Page 38: Unbelievable 'un'
unhappiest, **un**tidiest, **un**friendly, **un**fit, **un**healthy, **un**kind.

Page 39: Adding 'ed' and 'ing'
Jack finish**ed** his beans and wip**ed** the plate with toast. Then he look**ed** at the clock. He was late! Putt**ing** on his gloves, he went out. Soon he was runn**ing** onto the football pitch. After a few minutes, Jack scor**ed**! Everyone started cheer**ing**!

Page 40–41: More comprehension
1. Funtime Fair
2. Balloon Modeller
3. 3pm
4. £2

Page 42: Big, bigger
Tall**er**, Long**er**, Wis**er**, Happi**er**

Page 43: Biggest
Your answers may vary!

 Hungriest

 Fastest

 Smallest

 Longest

Slowest